CANALLIGATOR

BY

GIOVANNI

'SPOZ'

ESPOSITO

ILLUSTRATIONS BY

PURRL

PANKRAS

SCAN THE QR CODE TO TAKE YOU TO
SPOZ'S YOUTUBE CHANNEL, WHERE
YOU CAN VIEW A LITTLE FILM OF
EACH CHAPTER.

ISBN : 978-1-9997749-9-8

First published in 2021
by Caboodle Books

A Catalogue record for this book is available from the British Library.
Page Layout by Highlight Type Bureau Ltd, Leeds LS20 8LQ
Printed and bound by CPI Group (UK) Ltd, Croydon, CR0 4YY

The paper and board used in this book are natural recyclable products made from wood
grown in sustainable forests. The manufacturing processes conform to the
environmental regulations of the country of origin.

Caboodle Books Ltd.
Riversdale, 8 Rivock Avenue,
Steeton, BD20 6SA, UK.

Acknowledgements

Thank you to my young "focus group" ...
Tabitha Couch, Alice Birch, Danny Birch, Louie Molloy, Rosie Molloy,
Flynn Bovington and Caitlyn Bovington. You kids rock!
Oh ... and their moms are okay too.

Massive thanks to A.F. Harrold for his wise mentoring, which helped make Canalligator better than it was!

Massive musical thanks to Loz Rabone for the stunning soundtrack to Canalligator. Check out the YouTube films to hear the brilliantness of it!

Immense illustrative thanks to Libby Durose (aka Purrl Pankras) for the stunning comic book art that you will see on these pages.

Owen Craven Griffiths ... Berko ... nice one mate.

To all the poets, writers and artists of all forms and genres ...
Keep on being ace..

Thank you to the lovely people at Caboodle Books and Authors Abroad, for getting Canalligator out there ... you folks are ace!

Gotta say a big thank you to Arts Council England for funding the Canalligator project.

Thank Yous

This is a list of people who I really must say "thank you" to ...

Mama e Papa e la famiglia Esposito
My amazing wife, Claudia, for putting up with me!
My ace kids Zack and Fran

Dreadlockalien
AF Harrold
Lorna Mehan
Jodi Ann Bickley
John Hegley
Attila the Stockbroker
Stevie Camden (Polar Bear)
Poets, Prattlers and Pandemonialists

Elvis McGonagall
Johnny Fluffypunk
Jemima Hughes
Evrah Rose
John Cooper Clarke
Michael Rosen
Jacob Sam La Rose
Stuart Bartholomew and the gang at Verve.

Leon Priestnall ... RIP dude x

The brilliant gang at Caboodle Books and Authors Abroad. You folks are ace.

Everyone at Birmingham, Worcestershire and Midlands Libraries.

Arts Council England, who made this book possible

Apples and Snakes, especially Owen (that's two thank yous in one book dude!)

Daz Hale, Sonny and Shay and all the lovely people at BBC Radio WM

Kate Justice, Nina Das Gupta and all the lovely people at BBC Radio Hereford and Worcester.

To all the gang at Severn Arts, especially Steve and Debbie

All my poetry friends in and around Brum ... and beyond! You lovely, lovely people! You know who you are!

All the young people I've met at all the schools I've ever done (and yet to do) poetry workshops at.

All my teachers at St. James RC Primary School in Rubery

All my teachers at Archbishop Masterson's RC Secondary School in Northfield (now demolished).

... And anyone else that knows me.

Contents

FOR
LOLA

CHAPTER 1

AN ABSENT FRIEND

SCAN ME

CANALLIGATOR

SCAN THE QR CODE TO TAKE YOU TO SPOZ'S YOUTUBE CHANNEL,
WHERE YOU CAN VIEW A LITTLE FILM OF EACH CHAPTER.

MOHAMMED AND BILLY WERE BEST OF FRIENDS, THEY ALWAYS LOOKED OUT FOR EACH OTHER

YOU COULD SAY THAT THEY WERE MORE THAN MATES, LIKE... BROTHERS FROM ANOTHER MOTHER

THE LADS OFTEN PLAYED DOWN BY THE CANAL,

THOUGH THEIR MOMS HAD TOLD THEM NOT TO

BUT LIKE
SO MANY KIDS,
WHEN GROWN-UPS
SAY "NO",
IT'S MET WITH
A "WELL... I'VE
JUST GOT TO!"

THEY WERE
AWARE OF
THE DANGERS
OF PLAYING
NEAR WATER

THAT WAS
DEEPER
THAN
CHILDREN
MIGHT THINK

AND WHO
KNEW OF
THE
DEBRIS THAT
LURKED
UNDERNEATH?

IT WAS SCARY
TO FALL IN THE
DRINK!

NOW BILLY AND MO WERE SENSIBLE KIDS AND STAYED AWAY FROM THE EDGES

THEY STUCK TO THE TOW PATH AND LOOKED AT THE BIRDS, THAT WOULD NEST IN THE TREES AND THE HEDGES

THERE WAS ANOTHER THING THAT DREW THEM TO THE CANAL

A MEMORY THAT THEY'D HOLD TILL THE END, MONTHS MAY HAVE PASSED, THOUGH THEY'D NEVER FORGET

CASEY... THEIR LONG LOST FRIEND

11

12

14

WOULD SOMEONE, OR SOMETHING, HEAR THEIR CRIES?

WHO ROAMED THE BACK WATERS OF BRUM?

THE FOUR BULLIES TURNED WITH A MYSTIFIED LOOK

BUT THIS WAS THE LEAST OF THEIR TROUBLES!

THE CANAL WATER SWELLED WITH A TERRIBLE SWELL

...SMILED AT THEM BOTH

THEN GAVE THEM A WINK

THE BOYS' FEARS BEGAN TO TRANSFORM

SURELY THIS COULDN'T BE THE LIZARD THEY'D HAD,

THAT THEY'D FED AND LOVED AND KEPT WARM?

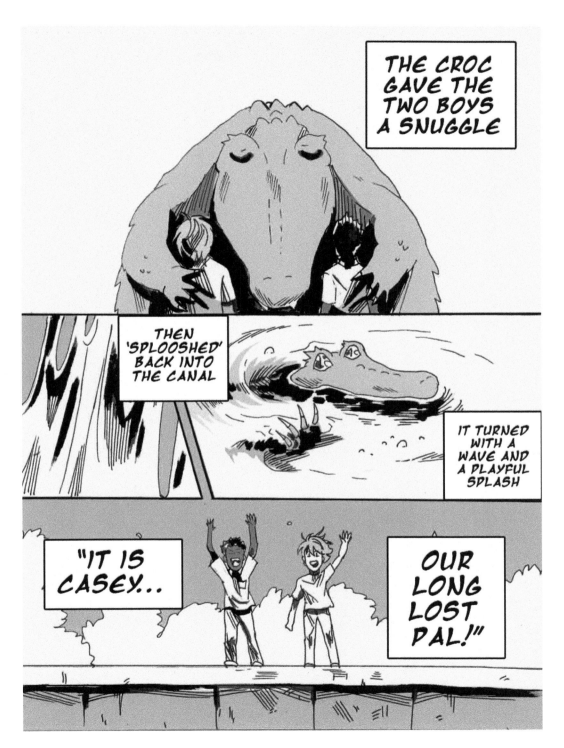

THE CROC GAVE THE TWO BOYS A SNUGGLE

THEN 'SPLOOSHED' BACK INTO THE CANAL

IT TURNED WITH A WAVE AND A PLAYFUL SPLASH

"IT IS CASEY...

OUR LONG LOST PAL!"

26

27

CHAPTER 2

SEVEN OR EIGHT MONTHS EARLIER

SCAN ME

CANALLIGATOR

SCAN THE QR CODE TO TAKE YOU TO SPOZ'S YOUTUBE CHANNEL,
WHERE YOU CAN VIEW A LITTLE FILM OF EACH CHAPTER.

BILLY LOVED REPTILES, THEY REALLY WERE HIS THING

AND OF ALL THE REPTILES BILLY LOVED, A LIZARD WOULD BE KING

SNAKES WERE COOL, OF COURSE THEY WERE

BUT THEY WERE A BIT TOO SCARY

AND HE WAS NEVER ONE FOR A BEARDED DRAGON

AS THEY MIGHT BE A BIT TOO HAIRY

SO HE SAVED AND SAVED HIS POCKET MONEY, TO MAKE HIS DREAM COME TRUE

SO HIS MOM AND DAD COULD BUY HIM A LIZARD ...

FROM A MAN THAT THEY BOTH KNEW

NOW...

THEY DIDN'T KNOW THE MAN WAS A FIBBER

THEY HAD NO OBVIOUS CLUES

HE KNEW THAT IT DID TO SOME YOUNG PEOPLE

THOUGH, BILLY THOUGHT THAT WAS JUST SILLY

HE WAS GOING TO NAME IT 'BRUTUS'

THOUGH IT SOUNDED A LITTLE BIT BRUTAL

SO HE DECIDED ON THE NAME 'CASEY'

BECAUSE THAT WAS MORE GENDER NEUTRAL

SO...
OFF TO
THE CUT,
A SAD
BILLY
WENT

KNOWING
FREEDOM
FOR CASEY
WAS BEST

HIS GOOD
FRIEND
MOHAMMED
WENT
ALONG TOO

IN CASE
BILLY
BECAME
DISTRESSED

FOR THIS WAS A NEW CHAPTER IN THIS LIZARD'S TALE

TO FIND OUT LIFE'S MEANING AND WORTH

BECAUSE NEITHER MOHAMMED, NOR BILLY HAD KNOWN

THAT CASEY HAD BEEN AN ALLIGATOR... SINCE BIRTH!

CHAPTER 3

BORN AGAIN... SORT OF

CANALLIGATOR

SCAN THE QR CODE TO TAKE YOU TO SPOZ'S YOUTUBE CHANNEL,
WHERE YOU CAN VIEW A LITTLE FILM OF EACH CHAPTER.

THE
BIRMINGHAM
CANALS
BECAME
CASEY'S
HOME

THE
ALLIGATOR
KEPT
WELL OUT
OF SIGHT

SWIMMING
THE DEPTHS
DURING
THE DAY

COMING
UP FOR AIR IN
THE NIGHT

44

CASEY ENJOYED GOBBLING FISH

AND SOMETIMES THE OCCASIONAL DUCK

THERE WERE EVEN GEESE THAT CASEY COULD SNATCH

WHEN OUR ALLIGATOR CAUGHT SOME LUCK

NIGHT TIMES WERE NOISY AROUND SOME PARTS OF BRUM

DANCING AND MUSIC WAS RIFE

SO CASEY WOULD SWIM TO THE QUIETER CORNERS

SO AS NOT TO DISTURB THE NIGHT LIFE

YET PEOPLE STILL CAME DOWN TO THE CANALS

TO JOG OR RIDE BIKES THAT WERE SPORTY

SO OUR ALLIGATOR TRIED TO STAY OUT OF THE WAY

BECAUSE EATING PEOPLE WAS NAUGHTY

AS THE WEEKS WENT BY, CASEY GOT BIGGER

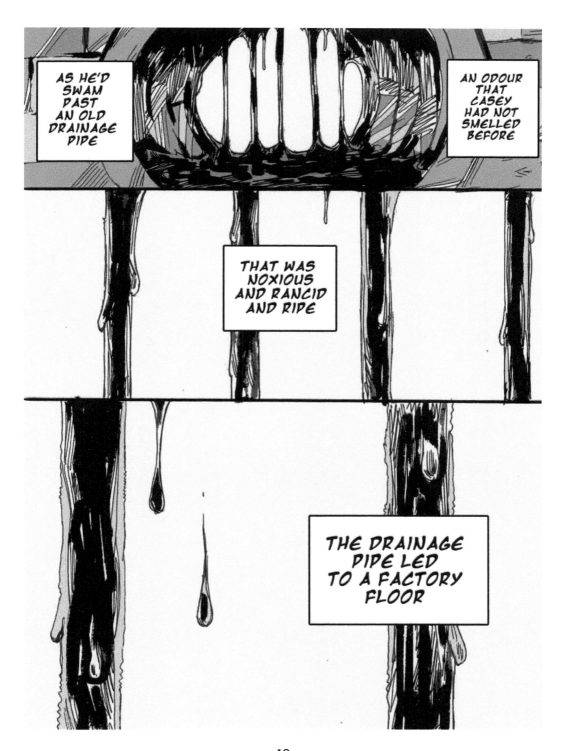

AS HE'D SWAM PAST AN OLD DRAINAGE PIPE

AN ODOUR THAT CASEY HAD NOT SMELLED BEFORE

THAT WAS NOXIOUS AND RANCID AND RIPE

THE DRAINAGE PIPE LED TO A FACTORY FLOOR

WHERE CHICKENS WERE BEING FED WEIRD STUFF

THERE WERE AWFUL MACHINES THAT FORCE FED THEM MORE, IF THE CHICKENS WEREN'T EATING ENOUGH

THE CHICKENS WOULD GROW TO IMMENSE PROPORTIONS, FAR BIGGER THAN ANY CHICKEN SHOULD

YOU COULD TELL THAT THE FACTORY WAS A TERRIBLE PLACE

AND THE BOSSES WERE UP TO NO GOOD

BUT THEY DIDN'T CARE, THERE WAS MONEY TO MAKE!

NOT BOTHERED ABOUT THE POLLUTION

THAT WOULD SLOWLY DRIBBLE INTO THE CANAL, CREATING A NASTY SOLUTION

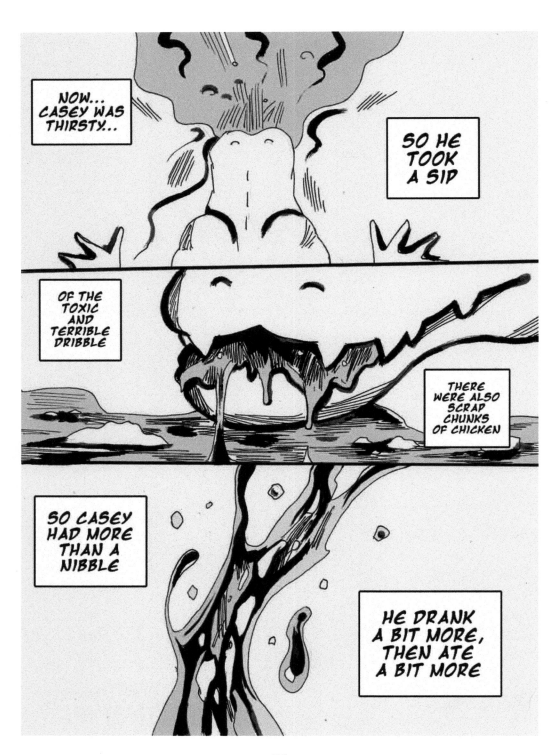

THE CHEMICALS HAD TURNED HIM INTO A MONSTER

POOR CASEY WENT INTO A SULK

HE WAS HAPPY BEING A GATOR, BUT NOW HE WAS AN INCROCABLE HULK!

OFF CASEY SWAM MAKING LOTS OF BIG WAVES

LIKE THE ROLLING WAKE OF A TIDE

HIS EXTERIOR WAS THAT OF A TERRIBLE BEAST

BUT HE WAS STILL A GOOD SOUL INSIDE

SO HE SANK TO THE DEPTHS OF THOSE BRUMMIE CANALS

LIKE A CUNNING AND COOL OPERATOR

THE LIZARD WAS GONE... A NEW 'THING' LIVED ON...

BIRMINGHAM'S CANALLIGATOR

CHAPTER 4

CANALLIGATOR MAKES NEW FRIENDS

SCAN ME

CANALLIGATOR

SCAN THE QR CODE TO TAKE YOU TO SPOZ'S YOUTUBE CHANNEL,
WHERE YOU CAN VIEW A LITTLE FILM OF EACH CHAPTER.

THEY WERE SO OVERJOYED THAT CASEY STILL LIVED

THAT HE'D SURVIVED AND THRIVED ALL ALONE

HE'D REMEMBERED THEM BOTH – AND THEY BOTH WERE AMAZED

AT HOW THEIR PET CASEY HAD GROWN

HE'D BEEN PRETTY BIG WHEN THEY'D BID HIM FAREWELL

AND SET THAT YOUNG LIZARD AFLOAT

TO SEE HIM AGAIN FILLED THEIR HEARTS WITH DELIGHT

EVEN THOUGH HE WAS AS BIG AS A BOAT!

AS MOHAMMED AND BILLY CONTINUED TO CHAT

THEY NOTICED NEW FACES AT PLAY

TWO GIRLS WERE STARTING IN THEIR CLASS

AND TODAY WAS THEIR VERY FIRST DAY

THEY PLAYED WITH EACH OTHER... AND NOBODY ELSE

THEY SEEMED A BIT NERVOUS AND SHY

SO BILLY AND MO, LOOKED AT EACH OTHER

AND SAID

LET'S GO OVER AND SAY 'HI'

64

65

66

BECAUSE NOT EVERYONE THEY'D MET AT THE SCHOOL

HAD REALLY BEEN ALL THAT NICE

WE'LL BE YOUR FRIENDS

MOHAMMED EXCLAIMED

AS THEY WALKED INTO SCHOOL TOGETHER

AND AT THE END OF THE DAY, THEIR SMILES WERE WARMER

IN SPITE OF THE COLD BRITISH WEATHER

THE WEEKS WENT BY AND THEIR FRIENDSHIPS GREW

BUT THE BOYS STILL HAD A SECRET THEY HELD

COULD THEY TELL TINA AND MIA ABOUT CASEY

NOW THAT THEIR FRIENDSHIP HAD GELLED?

SO...

ONE WEEKEND, THEY WENT TO THE CANAL

74

AS THE GIRLS MADE THEIR PROMISES, OUT POPPED A FOOT

FOLLOWED BY ANOTHER...

THEN A HEAD!

77

AND WITH A WINK OF HIS EYE AND A GRIN AND A 'SPLOOOOSH'

CANALLIGATOR WAS BACK IN THE WATER

HE GAVE THEM A SPLASH AND A WAVE OF HIS TAIL

TO SHOW THEM ALL, HE WAS HAPPY

THE GIRLS WAVED EXCITEDLY AS THEY REALISED

THEIR NEW FRIEND WOULD NEVER BE 'SNAPPY'

AS THEY WALKED HOME, THEY CHATTED AND CHATTED

WITHOUT THE NEED OF A TRANSLATOR

BILLY AND MIA AND TINA AND MO

TALKED OF CASEY...

THE CANALLIGATOR!!

CHAPTER 5

THE SECRET'S OUT

CANALLIGATOR

SCAN THE QR CODE TO TAKE YOU TO SPOZ'S YOUTUBE CHANNEL,
WHERE YOU CAN VIEW A LITTLE FILM OF EACH CHAPTER.

THE 'BIRMINGHAM MOLE' HAD PRINTED A STORY

BIRMINGHAM MOLE WHAT IS THE CREATURE?

OF A FEARSOME CREATURE THAT LURKED

THOSE FOUR BULLY BOYS HAD WANTED SOME FAME

AND THEIR TALE OF OUR CASEY HAD WORKED!

SOME CALLED IT 'CROCZILLA', SOME CALLED IT 'THE BEAST'

91

THE OTHER HUNTERS ALL LOOKED AFRAID

THEY ALL STARTED TO TURN AND TO LEAVE

THE 'CROC TERMINATOR' LAUGHED LIKE A WITCH

HE KNEW THEY WERE SCARED AND NAIVE

WITH ALL OF THEM GONE, HE STARTED TO GRIN

HIS MOOD BECAME MURDEROUS AND MEANER

THOUGH HE HADN'T REALLY NOTICED OUR FOUR YOUNG FRIENDS

BILLY, MO, MIA AND TINA

CHAPTER 6

THE GREAT ESCAPE

CANALLIGATOR

SCAN THE QR CODE TO TAKE YOU TO SPOZ'S YOUTUBE CHANNEL,
WHERE YOU CAN VIEW A LITTLE FILM OF EACH CHAPTER.

BILLY AND TINA JUMPED INTO HIS WAY

BUT HE KNOCKED THEM BOTH INTO THE DIRT

WHICH FILLED CASEY'S EYES WITH A FEARSOME RAGE...

TWO OF HIS FRIENDS LOOKED HURT!

CROC TERMINATOR WAS LAUNCHED INTO THE SKY

BY CANALLIGATOR'S AWESOME TAIL POWER

HE FLEW UP AND UP... CLEARING BUILDINGS AND BIRDS...

IT WAS TIME FOR OUR 'GATOR TO HIDE

THEY HURRIED ALONG TO THE EMPTY TRUCK

ALL CLAMBERING UP IN THE BACK

BILLY AND MO PULLED THE DOORS SHUT

AND EVERYTHING TURNED QUITE BLACK

CHAPTER 7

ANOTHER FAREWELL

SCAN ME

CANALLIGATOR

SCAN THE QR CODE TO TAKE YOU TO SPOZ'S YOUTUBE CHANNEL,
WHERE YOU CAN VIEW A LITTLE FILM OF EACH CHAPTER.

115

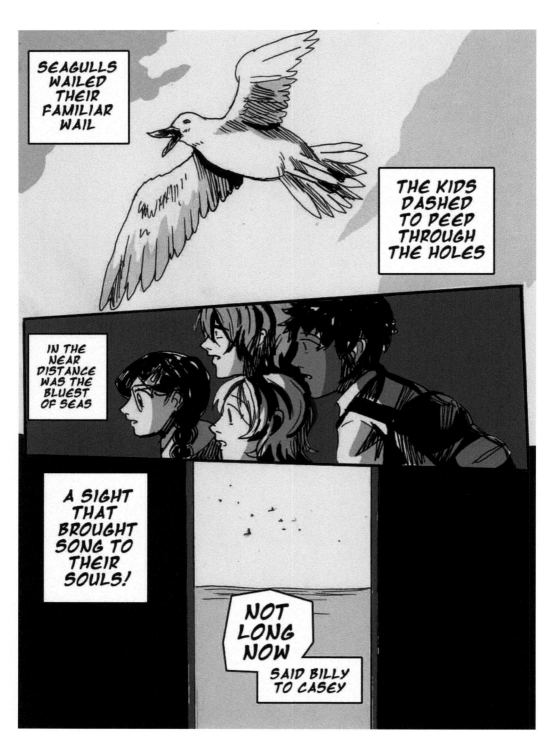

AS THEY SMILED THROUGH THEIR SADNESS AND PAIN

IN THEIR HEART OF HEARTS, THEY BOTH REALISED

THEY'D NOT SEE EACH OTHER AGAIN

A FEW MINUTES LATER MOHAMMED EXCLAIMED

WE'RE PULLING UP NEAR THE EDGE OF THE QUAY!

CASEY AND FRIENDS HAD ONE LAST GROUP HUG

119

121

123

AND STARTED TO MAKE THEIR WAY HOME

AFTER A WEEK OR TWO BACK IN BIRMINGHAM

OUR FOUR FRIENDS HAD SETTLED BACK DOWN

NOT QUITE WHAT HE HAD EXPECTED

HE FELT HE COULD SEE WHAT CASEY COULD SEE

COULD THE TWO OF THEM STILL BE 'CONNECTED'?

COULD THEY SHARE THEIR THOUGHTS FROM LAND TO SEA?

127

Chapter 1 "An Absent Friend"

Mohammed and Billy were best of friends,
They always looked out for each other,
You could say that they were more than mates,
Like ... brothers from another mother.
The lads often played down by the canal,
Though their moms had told them not to,
But like so many kids, when grown-ups say "No",
It's met with a "Well ... I've just got to!"
They were aware of the dangers of playing near water,
That was deeper than children might think
And who knew of the debris that lurked underneath?
It was scary to fall in the drink!

Now Billy and Mo were sensible kids
And stayed away from the edges,
They stuck to the tow path and looked at the birds,
That would nest in the trees and the hedges.
There was another thing that drew them to the canal,
A memory that they'd hold till the end,
Months may have passed, though they'd never forget,
Casey ... their long lost friend.

"How was he doing?" they asked themselves,
"Was our buddy still happy and well?
We haven't seen Casey for such a long time,
We wish there were ways we could tell."
Which is secretly why they went down to the cut,
To find evidence of Casey's existence,
They'd always look out for 'non standard' poop,
Or a giveaway sign in the distance.

But alas, their searching was all in vain,
They felt rather sad and rejected,
Losing a friend like their lovely pet,
Had made them feel worse than expected.

They hoped, one day, that Casey would come,
To soothe their worries and sadness,
Sometimes it seemed like the world was sick,
With a feverish anger and madness.

"Oi! You two! What are you looking at!?"
Screeched a voice, bristling with mischief,
Four undesirables stood on the path
And were waiting to dish out some grief.
"We don't want any trouble," a scared Billy said,
"Can't you just leave us alone?"
"No we won't! We're bigger than you,
So give us your money and phone!"

"Help! Please help!" Cried a desperate Mo,
With no clue of who might come,
Would someone, or something, hear their cries?
Who roamed the back waters of Brum?
The four bullies laughed "Ha! Save your breath,
There's nobody near who can hear,
We're tougher than you so give us your stuff,
Or the aftermath will be severe!"

But ... then ... came a few ripples ... then a small wave,
A bit of a splash ... and then bubbles,
The four bullies turned with a mystified look,
But this was the least of their troubles!
The canal water swelled with a terrible swell,
As though someone had busted a dam,
Then out lurched the foot of a gruesome beast ...
There was a monster in Birmingham!

Next came a snout with some snaggely teeth
And a growl to make people's spines shiver!
The four bullies' eyes filled with fear
And their legs went all of a quiver!

"Run!" cried one of them, "Leg it!" another,
As the other two let out a wail
And as they ran, they all got a smack,
From the creature's long, jagged tail!

The bullies were gone ... now ... Billy and Mo
Stared in awe at the reptile's size,
And as they froze in abject terror,
There came an unexpected surprise.

The beast ...

...smiled at them both ... then gave them a wink,
The boys' fears began to transform,
Surely this couldn't be the lizard they'd had,
That they'd fed and loved and kept warm?
The croc gave the two boys a snuggle,
Then 'splooshed' back into the canal,
It turned with a wave and a playful splash,
"It *is* Casey ... our long lost pal!"

But how on earth, had he got so huge!?
What on earth had he been consuming?
Surely it couldn't be good for you?
But I bet it would keep business booming!
Billy and Mo, rushed to their homes,
Chatting all the way back,
Their friend had returned to protect them
And saved them from an awful attack!

"Do you remember how upset we were?"
Said Billy to an excited Mo,
"When we hugged him goodbye and waved him away,
Seven or eight months ago?"

"I know!" said Mo, "Just look at him now!
I just knew that sooner or later
We'd meet him again and our friend would return,
Though not like a ... CANALLIGATOR!!"
"Cool name," said Billy "Thanks," said Mo,
"I'm pleased that you set him free."
"Me too" said Billy "... that name *is* cool,
But he'll always be Casey to me".

Chapter 2 "Seven Or Eight Months Earlier"

Billy loved reptiles, they really were his thing,
And of all the reptiles Billy loved, a lizard would be king.
Snakes were cool, of course they were,
But they were a bit too scary,
And he was never one for a Bearded Dragon,
As they might be a bit too hairy.

So he saved and saved his pocket money,
To make his dream come true,
So his mom and dad could buy him a lizard ...
From a man that they both knew.
Now ... they didn't know the man was a fibber,
They had no obvious clues,
That the lizard that he was selling,
Wasn't the kind that Billy would choose.

So they bought the lizard in good faith,
With the money in Billy's bank,
They took it home ... and Billy smiled,
Then placed it in a large glass tank.
He made the terrarium feel like home,
With branches and a warming light,
He fed it crickets and mealworms too
And gave it a cuddle each night.

He didn't know if his pet was a boy or a girl,
But that didn't matter to Billy,
He knew that it did to some young people,
Though, Billy thought that was just silly.
He was going to name it 'Brutus',
Though it sounded a little bit brutal,
So he decided on the name 'Casey',
Because that was more gender neutral.

Day after day, Billy fed Casey
And day after day Casey grew,
He bought bigger tanks ... and bigger tanks still,
'Till there was only one thing left to do.

"You'll have to dump it in the canal" said mom,
"You can give it a fond farewell,
It's out-grown every tank you've bought,
That poor lizard's life must be hell!"
So ... off to the cut, a sad Billy went,
Knowing freedom for Casey was best,
His good friend Mohammed went along too,
In case Billy became distressed.

"Don't worry Billy" said a kind hearted Mo,
"Let's give Casey one final hug",
And as they group hugged their tearful goodbyes,
Casey slipped into the canal ... with a "glug".
Casey swam slowly ... and then turned around,
To give his two friends one last wave,
Remembering all of the warmth and love
Made Casey feel confident and brave.

For this was a new chapter in this lizard's tale,
To find out life's meaning and worth,
Because neither Mohammed, nor Billy had known,
That Casey had been an alligator ... since birth!

Chapter 3 "Born Again ... Sort Of"

The Birmingham canals became Casey's home,
The alligator kept well out of sight,
Swimming the depths during the day,
Coming up for air in the night.
Casey enjoyed gobbling fish
And sometimes the occasional duck,
There were even geese that Casey could snatch,
When our alligator caught some luck.

Night times were noisy around some parts of Brum,
Dancing and music was rife,
So Casey would swim to the quieter corners,
So as not to disturb the night life.
Yet people still came down to the canals,
To jog or ride bikes that were sporty,
So our alligator tried to stay out of the way,
Because eating people was naughty!

As the weeks went by, Casey got bigger
As did our reptile's appetite,
So Casey decided to go on a mission,
To find a more filling bite.

He'd noticed a smell ... a curious whiff,
As he'd swam past an old drainage pipe,
An odour that Casey had not smelled before,
That was noxious and rancid and ripe.
The drainage pipe led to a factory floor,
Where chickens were being fed weird stuff,
There were awful machines that force fed them more,
If the chickens weren't eating enough.

The chickens would grow to immense proportions,
Far bigger than any chicken should,
You could tell that the factory was a terrible place
And the bosses were up to no good.

But they didn't care, there was money to make!
Not bothered about the pollution,
That would slowly dribble into the canal,
Creating a nasty solution.

Now ... Casey was thirsty ... so he took a sip,
Of the toxic and terrible dribble,
There were also scrap chunks of chicken,
So Casey had more than a nibble.
He drank a bit more, then ate a bit more,
He scoffed and he swilled and he slurped
And when Casey had gobbled up quite enough,
Our charming young reptile burped!

A few hours later, Casey felt ... odd,
His snout and eyes started to swell,
His torso grew broader and longer and stronger
And the rest of him did as well!
The chemicals had turned him into a monster,
Poor Casey went into a sulk,
He was happy being a 'gator,
But now he was an incrocable hulk!

Off Casey swam making lots of big waves,
Like the rolling wake of a tide,
His exterior was that of a terrible beast,
But he was still a good soul inside.
So he sank to the depths of those Brummie canals,
Like a cunning and cool operator,
The lizard was gone ... a new 'thing' lived on ...
Birmingham's CANALLIGATOR!!

Chapter 4 "Canalligator Makes New Friends"

Monday came round as Mondays do,
Mo and Billy were back at school,
They talked and talked about their weekend,
Which had been frightening ... exciting and cool!

They were so overjoyed that Casey still lived
That he'd survived and thrived all alone,
He'd remembered them both – and they both were amazed,
At how their pet Casey had grown!
He'd been pretty big when they'd bid him farewell
And set that young lizard afloat,
To see him again filled their hearts with delight,
Even though he was as big as a boat!

As Mohammed and Billy continued to chat,
They noticed new faces at play,
Two girls were starting in their class
And today was their very first day.
They played with each other ... and nobody else,
They seemed a bit nervous and shy,
So Billy and Mo, looked at each other
And said "Let's go over and say 'hi'"

When the boys got closer, Billy said "Hi,
Is today your very first day?"
The girls turned and smiled a cautious smile,
Not really knowing what they should say.
"We not talk English very well,"
Said a shy voice, shallow and meek,
"We come from Italy just last month
And English we still learn to speak"

"WHAT ... ARE ... YOUR ... NAMES?" asked Mohammed intently,
In a tone that was loud and slow,
Because everyone knows it makes English easy
And that included our Mo.

"My name is Cristina, but Tina is fine
And this is my cousin called Mia."
"We're pleased to meet you, I'm Billy, that's Mo
And we're glad to welcome you here!"

The girls looked at each other and smiled again,
Though still wary, to be quite precise,
Because not everyone they'd met at the school,
Had really been all that nice.
"We'll be your friends" Mohammed exclaimed
As they walked into school together
And at the end of the day, their smiles were warmer,
In spite of the cold British weather.

The weeks went by and their friendships grew,
But the boys still had a secret they held,
Could they tell Tina and Mia about Casey,
Now that their friendship had gelled?
So ... one weekend, they went to the canal,
In spite of their previous menace,
Where Billy and Mo had real pleasure in saying,
"Brum's got more canals than Venice!"

As they walked and talked their way to the cut,
The subject of Casey was mentioned,
"So he is big lizard?" asked Cristina
"But he is ... how you say ... well intentioned?"
"Well done!" said Mo, "You've learnt a new word!"
"Bravissima!" Mia announced.
But as they laughed and said "hooray!"
Some horrible bullies pounced!

"Not you two again!?" said one of the thugs,
"But this time you've got girly girlies!
No crocodile now to save your skin,
We've got you by the short and curlies!"
"Help Casey! Help!" yelled Mo once again,
Just like he had done before,

But this time ... no ripples ... this time ... no waves ...

But in the distance ...

... a blood curdling "ROAR!"

The bullies went pale and started to run,
They knew what the roaring sound meant,
They all ran again, as fast as they could,
Before Casey could latch onto their scent.
The canal went quiet ... just the boys and girls left,
Though the girls were nervous and wary,
They had seen many lizards in Italy before,
Though none that had sounded this scary!

"It's okay," said Billy "No need to be scared,"
As the canal began to bubble and swell.
"Casey's our friend, he'll never hurt you
But please promise us you won't tell?"
As the girls made their promises, out popped a foot,
Followed by another ... then a head!
And as Canalligator rose to the bank,
The girls' eyes filled up with dread!

"Casey! We've missed you!" said a confident Billy
And stroked the wet beast on his snout.
Mohammed came forward and gave Casey a hug,
They were *really* best buddies ... no doubt!
The girls looked on, still slightly alarmed,
With a nervous and cautious demeanour.
"These are our friends," said Billy to Casey
"They're Italian – that's Mia ... that's Tina"

"Ciao," said Tina. "Buon giorno," said Mia,
Then Casey gave them a smile
"He likes you," said Billy, so they both smiled back,
"He's not made new friends in a while!"

Casey gave them a purr and a friendly snort,
As he could be a bit of a snorter
And with a wink of his eye and a grin and a 'sploooosh',
Canalligator was back in the water.

He gave them a splash and a wave of his tail,
To show them all, he was happy,
The girls waved excitedly as they realised,
Their new friend would never be 'snappy'.
As they walked home, they chatted and chatted,
Without the need of a translator,
Billy and Mia and Tina and Mo,
Talked of Casey ... THE CANALLIGATOR!!

Chapter 5 "The Secret's Out"

What a weekend! School was going to be great,
For Mo, Mia, Billy and Tina,
They just couldn't wait to see each other again,
They really could not have been keener!
So much talk about Casey, their friend,
Though the girls were, at first, petrified,
Was now their guardian and with just a call,
Would always be there at their side.

Monday flew by and Tuesday did too,
But Wednesday ... was like a blow to the gut,
As gossip was spreading around the school,
Of a monster that lived in the cut.
The 'Birmingham Mole' had printed a story,
Of a fearsome creature that lurked,
Those four bully boys had wanted some fame
And their tale of our Casey had worked!

Some called it 'Croczilla', some called it 'The Beast',
Some said it had eaten their dog,
Some said it had come from Tolkien's land,
Of The Lickey Hills or Moseley Bog.
But one thing was sure – the secret was out
And Casey would face an ordeal!
It wouldn't take long to track down our friend,
As his size was quite hard to conceal!

Mia and Billy and Tina and Mo,
Knew that Casey would need to be warned,
For the words that the paper put on the front page,
Meant our friend would be hated and scorned!
So many things that folks didn't understand,
Were often treated like this,
Resorting to fear, rage and disgust
Instead of tolerance and bliss.

So ... off they ran, straight after school,
To warn Casey of his fate,
Though as they reached those Brummie canals,
They sensed they'd arrived ... too late.
Hunters with hooks and gadgets and spears,
Were stalking the Canalligator,
There was even a nasty man with a coat
That was labelled 'Croc Terminator'!

He held a harpoon with a devil's tail point,
The light glistened bright on its end,
He wore dark glasses and spoke with a snarl,
That was made to distress and offend.
"I'll kill this beast," he said with a growl,
"The rest of you stay out of my way,
I've slaughtered crocs many times before,
It'll be dead by the end of the day!"

The other hunters all looked afraid,
They all started to turn and to leave,
The 'Croc Terminator' laughed like a witch,
He knew they were scared and naive.
With all of them gone, he started to grin
His mood became murderous and meaner,
Though he hadn't really noticed our four young friends,
Billy, Mo, Mia and Tina.

They needed a plan to help Casey escape
The Croc Terminator's harpoon,
He'd promised results by the end of the day
And it was already late afternoon.
They'd noticed a truck parked up near by
With doors open ... completely unloaded,
But they'd need to call Casey and create a diversion,
So that's exactly what our young Mo did.

Chapter 6 "The Great Escape"

"Mia! Quick! Mia, run with me up here"
Mo half whispered, taking her by the hand
And as they ran up the tow path, Mo explained,
Exactly the plan he had planned.
They laughed and they joked, running up the canal,
Catching the Croc Terminator's eye,
And just when they thought they were far enough away,
Mia let out a scream and a cry!

"Aiuto! Aiuto!" yelped Mia in Italian,
As Mohammed fell into the water,
"This is just what I need," thought the Croc Terminator,
"He's the bait in this big beastie's slaughter!"

He grasped his weapon and made for the kids,
Expecting the beast to come soon,
"That boy's splashing will attract the croc
And I'll skewer it with my harpoon!"

"This is my chance!" Billy thought to himself,
While the hunter went in the other direction,
"I just need to call Casey, lead him into the truck
And make sure we're avoiding detection"
So Billy put his head right under the water
And yelled "Hey! Casey! Come here!"
Then shortly, Tina saw ripples and waves
And she knew Canalligator was near!

A snout broke the surface ... then two grapefruit eyes,
Then a head as big as a door ...
"Shhhhh," said Tina ... "Come up," said Billy,
As they helped our huge lizard ashore.
Billy and Tina's hearts thumped like a drum,
Determined their plan wouldn't fail,
Though as Casey scrambled out of the canal,
He rashly lashed out with his tail.

"SPLOOSH!" went his tail into the canal ...
The Croc Terminator jerked round!
He grabbed his harpoon and with a shrill cry,
Set off like a racing greyhound!
Billy and Tina jumped into his way,
But he knocked them both into the dirt,
Which filled Casey's eyes with a fearsome rage ...
Two of his friends looked hurt!

As Croc Terminator leapt with his harpoon,
Like the bad guy in a comic strip,
Canalligator roared and spun on his toes,
Then his massive tail cracked like a whip!

Croc Terminator was launched into the sky
By Canalligator's awesome tail power,
He flew up and up ... clearing buildings and birds ...
And over Brum's Post Office Tower!

With the hunter gone, Casey looked for his friends,
Mo and Mia ran back to his side,
Billy and Tina picked themselves up,
It was time for our 'gator to hide.
They hurried along to the empty truck,
All clambering up in the back,
Billy and Mo pulled the doors shut,
And everything turned quite black.

Chapter 7 "Another Farewell"

Small shafts of light snuck into the truck,
As it drove for three hours or four,
The kids took turns to peep through the gaps,
To see if they could see the sea shore.
"What if we're not heading for the coast?" quizzed Mo,
"Please no say that!" pleaded Mia,
Then came a sound they all recognised,
And they knew that the ocean was near.

Seagulls wailed their familiar wail,
The kids dashed to peep through the holes,
In the near distance was the bluest of seas,
A sight that brought song to their souls!
"Not long now," said Billy to Casey,
As they smiled through their sadness and pain,
In their heart of hearts, they both realised,
They'd not see each other again.

A few minutes later Mohammed exclaimed
"We're pulling up near the edge of the quay!"
Casey and friends had one last group hug,
For in a moment, our beast would be free!
The door was locked ... but that didn't matter,
Casey had the strength to terrify,
With a swipe of his tail, the doors opened wide
And it was time to say 'goodbye'.

He leapt from the truck and across the quay
And plunged into the water below,
He swam out to sea, then turned for his friends,
So they could witness his 'fond farewell' show.
He breached into the air with a playful roar
Somersaulting and spinning so fast ...
And then he was gone ... under the waves
Canalligator ... free ... at last!

Our four friends stood and watched the display,
As Casey went under clouds of sea foam,
They looked at each other with tearful eyes
And started to make their way home.
After a week or two back in Birmingham
Our four friends had settled back down,
They went back to school and their daily routines
In that wonderful place called Brum Town.

But ... Billy had dreams that felt a bit odd,
Not quite what he had expected,
He felt he could see what Casey could see
Could the two of them still be 'connected'?
Could they share their thoughts from land to sea?
Had their brains, somehow, gotten greater?
Was this the end ... or just the beginning?
For Billy ... and CANALLIGATOR!!

A Bit About the Author ... Spoz

SPOZ...was born in Rubery, on the edge of Birmingham in 1964. He became known as 'Spoz' (like his brothers and sister and cousin) because it was easier than his real name, 'GIOVANNI ESPOSITO' and happens to be the bit between the 'E' and the 'ito' (sort of).

SPOZ...is an award winning performance poet, singer / songwriter, film maker, playwright and is the poet-in-residence at Birmingham City FC. He has been seen on BBC and Central Television, has written for, and been heard on BBC Radio Four, Radio Five Live, Radio West Midlands, Radio Coventry & Warwickshire, Capital Gold and on the toilet. Spoz has performed at the Glastonbury festival, Cheltenham Literature festival, Oxford Literature Festival, Warwick Words festival, Ledbury Poetry Festival, Bartons Arms Comedy Club, the Shambala festival and in front of his mom.

SPOZ...was 'crowned' Birmingham's eleventh poet laureate in October 2006. He continues to work extensively in schools, lifting the appeal of writing and performing poetry to hitherto, unseen heights.

SPOZ... remains modest and still lives in Birmingham.

SPOZ ... looks a bit like Joe Pasquale.